AUCASSIN AND NICOLETTE

AUCASSIN AND NICOLETTE

Francis William Bourdillon

www.General-Books.net

Publication Data:

Title: Aucassin and Nicolette
Author: Francis William Bourdillon
General Books publication date: 2009
Original publication date: 1903
Description: Inscription in front read: To Prof. York Powell from Lucien Pissarro. 16.6.1903.
Subjects: French poetry

How We Made This Book for You
We made this book exclusively for you using patented Print on Demand technology.
First we scanned the original rare book using a robot which automatically flipped and photographed each page.
We automated the typing, proof reading and design of this book using Optical Character Recognition (OCR) software on the scanned copy. That let us keep your cost as low as possible.
If a book is very old, worn and the type is faded, this can result in typos or missing text. This is also why our books don't have illustrations; the OCR software can't distinguish between an illustration and a smudge.
We understand how annoying typos, missing text or illustrations or an index that doesn't work, can be. That's why we provide a free digital copy of most books exactly as they were originally published. Simply go to our website (www.general-books.net) to check availability. And we provide a free trial membership in our book club so you can get free copies of other editions or related books.
OCR is not a perfect solution but we feel it's more important to make books available for a low price than not at all. So we warn readers on our website and in the descriptions we provide to book sellers that our books don't have illustrations and may have typos or missing text. We also provide excerpts from each book to book sellers and on our website so you can preview the quality of the book before buying it.
If you would prefer that we manually type, proof read and design your book so that it's perfect, we are happy to do that. Simply contact us for the cost.

Limit of Liability/Disclaimer of Warranty:
The publisher and author make no representations or warranties with respect to the accuracy or completeness of the book. The advice and strategies in the book may not be suitable for your situation. You should consult with a professional where appropriate. The publisher is not liable for any damages resulting from the book.
Please keep in mind that the book was written long ago; the information is not current. Furthermore, there may be typos, missing text or illustration and explained above.

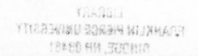

CONTENTS

1

SECTION 1

THE NEW LIFE
  DANTE ALIGHIERI Italian Text with English Translation
  EDITED BY
  LUIGI RICC1
  *Foolscap*8v0,*2s, net in doth;net in leather*
  LondonKeganPaul, Trench, Trubner&Co., Ltd.

2

SECTION 2

UNIFORM WITH THIS VOLUME
  6:/.net in cloth; 2s. net in leather
  THE LIGHT OF ASIA
  EdwinArnold
  THE SONG CELESTIAL
  EdwinArnold
  THE QUATRAINS OF OMAR
  KHAYYAN
  Whinfield
  TEXTS FROM THE BUDDHIST CANON
  (DHAMMAPADA)
  Translated from the Chinese
  SamuelBeal
  THE BREITMANN BALLADS
  CharlesLeland
  CANTEMUS DOMINO
  A little book of Canticles
  LondonKecanPaul, Trench, Trubner&Co., Ltd.

AUCASSIN AND NICOLETTE AUCASSIN AND NICOLETTE
THE OLD FRENCH TEXT
For ordinary reading
AUCASSIN AND NICOLETTE
Edited and Translated by F. W. Bourdili. on,
M. A., with Notes and Glossary
*Second Edition. Fcap*8vo. yj. 60.
MACMILLAN & CO.
– A/Vw-
*For paleeographical purposes*CEST DAUCASIN ET DE NICOLETE Reproduced
in photo-facsimile and type- transliteration from the unique MS. at Paris, by the care
of F. W. Bourdillon, M. A.
4/0. 15.
CLARENDONPRESS, OXFORD
AUCASSIN
AND NICOLETTE
TRANSLATEDFROM
FRENCH
FRANCIS WILLIAM
BOURDILLON
LONDON
KEGAN PAUL, TRENCH, TRUBNER & CO. LTD
PATERNOSTER HOUSE, CHAR1NO CROSS ROAD
IQOJ
INTRODUCTION
story of Love, that simple theme with variations*ad libitum, ad iiifinitum,*is never
old, never stale, never out-of-date. And as we sometimes seek rest from the brilliant
audacities and complex passions of Wagner or Tschaikowsky in the tender simplicity
of some ancient English air, so we occasionally turn with relief from the wit and
insight and subtlety of our modern novelists to the old uncomplicated tales of faerie
or romance, and find them after all more moving, more tender, even more real, than
all the laboured realism of these photographic days. And here before us is of all pretty
love-stories perhaps the prettiest. Idyllic as Daphnis and Chloe, romantic as Romeo
and Juliet, tender as Undine, remote as Cupid and Psyche, yet with perpetualtouches
of actual life, and words that raise pictures; and lightened all through with a dainty
playfulness, as if Ariel himself had hovered near all the time of its writing, and Puck
now and again shot a whisper of suggestion.

Yet it is only of late years that the charm of this story has been truly appreciated.
Composed probably in Northern France, about the close of the twelfth century, – the
time of our own Angevin kings and the most brilliant period of Old-French literature,
– it has survived only in a single manuscript of later date, where it is found hidden
among a number of tales in verse less pleasing in subject and far less delightful in
form. There it had lain unknown till discovered by M. de Sainte-Palaye, and printed
by him in modernised French in 1752, one hundred and fifty years ago. There is no

3

SECTION 3

AUCASSIN &? NICOLETTE
   'TIS OF AUCASSIN AND OF
NICOLETTE
would list a pleasant lay,
Pastime of the old and grey?
Of two lovers, children yet,
Aucassin and Nicolette;
Of the sorrows he went through,
Of the great things he did do,
All for his bright favoured may.
Sweet the song is, fair the say,
Full of art and full of grace.
There is none in such ill case,
Sad with sorrow, waste with care,
Sick with sadness, if he hear,
But shall in the hearing be
Whole again and glad with glee,
So sweet the story.

'5

Here they speak and tell the story

How Bulgarius Count of Valence made war upon Warren Count of Beaucaire. And this war was so great, so marvellous, and so mortal, that not a day dawned but there he was before the city, at the gates, at the walls, at the fences, with knights a hundred and men-at-arms ten thousand on foot and on horse; and he burned his land, laid waste his country, and slew his liegemen. Warren, Count of Beaucaire, was an old man and feeble, who had overlived his term. He had none to succeed him, neither son nor daughter, save one only boy; and what he was like, I will tell you. Aucassin was the young lord's name, and a pretty lad he was. He had golden hair in little curls, and laughing blue eyes, a face fair of colour and fine of curve, and a proud shapely nose. Aye, so endued was he with good conditions that there was none bad in him, but good only. But so overcome was he of Love, who masters all, that he refused knighthood, abjured arms, shunned the tourney, and left undone all his devoir.

His father and his mother would say to him: " Son! come, take thine arms and to horse!Fight for thy land and succour thy liegemen! If they see thee in the midst of them, they will fight the better for their lives and their havings and for thy land and mine! "

" Father," said Aucassin, " to what purpose is this oration? Never God give me ought that I ask of Him, if I take knighthood or mount horse, if I face fight or battlefield to smite knight or be myself smitten, if you give me not Nicolette, my sweet friend whom I love so well! "

" My son," said his father, " it cannot be. Have done with Nicolette! She is a slave-girl, carried captive from a foreign land. The Viscount of this place bought her of the heathen, and brought her here. He held her at the font, and christened her, and stood godfather to her. Some day he will give her a young fellow to win bread for her in wedlock. What is this to you? If you want a wife, I will give you a king's daughter or a count's. There is never so rich a man in France but you shall have his daughter, it you want her."

" Alack, father! " said Aucassin. " Where now is honour on earth so high, which Nicolette my sweet friend would not grace if it were hers? Were she Empress of Constantinopleor of Germany, were she Queen of France or of England, there were but little in it, so noble is she and gracious and debonair and endued with all good conditions."

Here they sing.

Aucassinwas of Beaucaire;
His was the fine castle there;
But on slender Nicolette
Past man's moving is he set,
Whom his father doth refuse;
Menace did his mother use:
" Out upon thee, foolish boy!
Nicolette is but a toy,
Castaway from Carthagen,
Bought a slave of heathen men.

If for marrying thou be,
Take a wife of high degree! "
" Mother, 1 will none but her.
Hath she not the gentle air,
Grace of limb, and beauty bright?
I am snared in her delight.
If I love her 'tis but meet,
So passing sweet! "
Here they speak and tell the story.
WhenWarren Count of Beaucaire perceived that Aucassin his son was not to be moved from his love of Nicolette, he betook him to the Viscount of the place, who was his liegeman; and addressed him thus:

" Sir Viscount, come, rid me of Nicolette your god-daughter! A curse on the land whence ever she was fetched to this country! Now Aucassin is lost to me, and all because of her. He refuses knighthood and leaves undone all his devoir. Rest assured that if I can get hold of her I will burn her in a fire; and for yourself too you may fear the worst."

" Sir," said the Viscount, " 'tis grief to me that he go to her, or come to her, or speak to her. I had bought her with my poor pieces. I had held her at the font, and christened her, and stood god-father to her; and I would have given her a young fellow to win bread for her in wedlock. What is this to Aucassin your son? But seeing your will is so and your good pleasure, I will send her to such a land and to such a country that he shall never set eyes on her more."

" See you do so! " said Count Warren. " Else it might go ill with you."

Thus they parted. Now the Viscount was a very rich man, and had a fine palace with a garden before it. He had Nicolette put in a room there, on an upper storey, with an old woman for company; and he had bread put there, and meat and wine and all they needed. Then he had the door locked, so that there was no way to get in or out. Only there was a window of no great size which looked on the garden and gave them a little fresh air.

Here they sing.
Nicoletteis prisoner,
In a vaulted bed-chamber,
Strange of pattern and design,
Richly painted, rarely fine.
At the window-sill of stone
Leaned the maiden sad and lone.
Yellow was her shining hair,
And her eyebrow pencilled rare,
Face fine-curved and colour fair:
Never saw you lovelier.
Gazed she o'er the garden-ground,
Saw the opening roses round,
Heard the birds sing merrily;
Then she made her orphan cry:

" Woe's me! what a wretch am I!
Caged and captive, why, ah why?
Aucassin, young lord, prithee,
Your sweetheart, am I not she?
Ay, methinks you hate not me.
For your sake I'm prisoner,
In this vaulted bed-chamber,
Where my life's a weary one.
But by God, sweet Mary's son,
Long herein I will not stay,
Can I find way! "

Here they speak and tell the story.

Nicolettewas in prison, as you have harkened and heard, in the chamber. The cry and the noise ran through all the land and through all the country that Nicolette was lost. There are some say she is fled abroad out of the land. Other some that Warren, Count of Beaucaire, has had her done to death. Rejoice who might, Aucassin was not well pleased. But he wentstraightway to the Viscount of the place, and thus addressed him:

" Sir Viscount, what have you done with Nicolette, my very sweet friend, the thing that I love best in all the world? Have you stolen and taken her from me? Rest assured that if I die of this thing, my blood will be required of you; and very justly, when you have gone and killed me with your two hands. For you have stolen from me the thing that I love best in all the world."

" Fair sir," said the Viscount, " now let be! Nicolette is a slave-girl whom I fetched from a foreign land and bought for money of the heathen. I held her at the font, and christened her and stood godfather to her, and have brought her up. One of these days I would have given her a young fellow to win bread for her in wedlock. What is this to you? Take you some king's daughter or some count's. Moreover, what were you profited, think you, had you made her your concubine, or taken her to live with you? Mighty little had you got by that, seeing that your soul would be in Hell for ever and ever, for to Paradise you would never win! "

" Paradise? What have I to do there? I seek not to win Paradise, so I have Nicolettemy sweet friend whom I love so well. For none go to Paradise but I'll tell you who. Your old priests and your old cripples, and the halt and maimed, who are down on their knees day and night, before altars and in old crypts; these also that wear mangy old cloaks, or go in rags and tatters, shivering and shoeless and showing their sores, and who die of hunger and want and cold and misery. Such are they who go to Paradise; and what have I to do with them? Hell is the place for me. For to Hell go the fine churchmen, and the fine knights, killed in the tourney or in some grand war, the brave soldiers and the gallant gentlemen. With them will I go. There go also the fair gracious ladies who have lovers two or three beside their lord. There go the gold and the silver, the sables and ermines. There go the harpers and the minstrels and the kings of the earth. With them will I go, so I have Nicolette my most sweet friend with me."

" I' faith," said the Viscount, "'tis but vain to speak of it; you will see her no more. Aye, were you to get speech of her and it came to your father's ears, he would burn both her and me in a fire; and for yourself too you might fear the worst."

" This is sore news to me," said Aucassin. And he departed from the Viscount, sorrowful.

Here they sing.

Aucassinhas turned once more
In wanhope and sorrow sore
For his love-friend bright of face.
None can help his evil case,
None a word of counsel say.
To the palace went his way;
Step by step he climbed the stair;
Entered in a chamber there.
Then he 'gan to weep alone,
And most dismally to groan,
And his lady to bemoan.
" Nicolette, ah, gracious air!
Coming, going, ever fair!
In thy talk and in thy toying,
In thy jest and in thy joying,
In thy kissing, in thy coying.
I am sore distressed for thee.
Such a woe has come on me
That I trow not to win free.
Sweet sister friend! "

Here they speak and tell the story.

the same time that Aucassin was in the chamber, bemoaning Nicolette his friend, Bulgarius Count of Valence, who had his war to maintain, forgat it not; but he had summoned his men, foot and horse, and advanced to assault the castle. And the cry went up and the noise; and the knights and men-at-arms girt on their armour, and hastened to the gates and walls to defend the castle; while the townsfolk mounted the parapets and hurled bolts and sharpened stakes. At the time when the assault was fast and furious, Warren Count of Beaucaire came into the chamber where Aucassin was weeping and bemoaning Nicolette his most sweet friend whom he loved so well.

"Ah, my son!" said he. "Wretch that thou art and unhappy, to see assault made on this thy castle – none better nor more strong! Know, moreover, that if thou lose it thou losest thine inheritance! Come now, my son, take thine arms and to horse! Fight for thy land, and succour thy liegemen, and get thee to the field! Though thou strike never a man nor be thyself stricken, if they but see thee among them they will make a better fight for their lives and their havings, and for thy land and mine. So tall art thou and so strong, 'tis no great thing to do; and it is thy devoir."

" Father," said Aucassin, " to what purpose is this oration? Never God give me ought that I ask of him, if I take knighthood or mount horse or go to the fighting to smite knight or be myself smitten, if you give me not Nicolette, my sweet friend, whom I love so well! "

"Son," said his father, "that cannot be. Rather would I suffer loss of all my inheritance, aye, of all I have, than that thou shouldst have her to woman or to wife! "

And he turned to go. And when Aucassin saw him departing, he called him back.

" Father," said Aucassin, " come hither, and I will make a fair covenant with you! "

" Aye, and what covenant, fair son? "

" I will take arms and go to the fighting on such condition, that, if God bring me again safe and sound, you will give me leave to see Nicolette my sweet friend for such time as T may speak two words to her or three, and once only kiss her."

" I consent," said his father.

So he made agreement with him, and Aucassin was well-pleased.

Here they sing.

Aucassinheard of the kiss
On returning to be his.
Hundred thousand marks pure gold
Him had made less blithe and bold.
Arms he called for, rich and rare j
They made ready for his wear.
Hauberk donned he, double-lined;
Helmet on his head did bind;
Girt his sword with hilt pure gold;
Mounted on his charger bold;
Spear and buckler then he took;
At his two feet cast a look,
In the stirrups trod they trim;
Wondrous proud he carried him.
His sweet friend – he thought on her,
To his charger clapped the spur;
Forth he springs full mettlesome;
Straightway to the gate they come
That led to battle.

Here they speak and tell the story.

Aucassinwas arrayed and mounted on his horse, as you have barkened and heard. Lord! how well it became him – the shield on his neck and the helm on his head and the sword-belt on his left hip! And the boy was tall and strong and comely and slim and well-grown; and the horse he bestrode was fleet of foot and high of mettle, and the boy had put him through the gate cleverly. Now don't you suppose that his thoughts would have been set on taking spoil of oxen or cows or goats? that he would have struck at some knight or been stricken in turn? Not a whit! it never once occurred to him. But his thought was so set upon Nicolette, his sweet friend, that he forgot the reins and all he had to do. And his horse, feeling the spur, dashed with him through the press, and charged right into the thick of the enemy, who laid hands on him on all sides, and made him prisoner. They took from him shield and lance, and led him captive then and there. They were already questioning one with another as to what manner of death they should put him to; and when Aucassin heard it.

" Ah, gracious Heaven! " he said, " and are these my mortal foes who hale me here and are presently about to cut off my head? And once I have my head cut off, nevermore shall I speak to Nicolette my sweet friend whom I love so well. Nay, I have yet a good sword, and under me a good steed untired. An I defend me not now for her sake, ne'er help her God if ever again she love me! "

The boy was tall and strong, and the horse beneath him was eager. He put his hand to his sword and began to strike to right and to left, slashing helmet and nose-guard, fist and wrist, and making havoc all around him as the boar does when the dogs set on him in the forest; so that he overthrew ten of their knights and wounded seven; and charged then and there out of the press, and rode back full gallop, sword in hand.

liulgarius, Count of Valence, heard say that they were about to hang Aucassin his enemy, and came that way. Aucassin failed not to espy him; and gripping his sword, he smote him through the helmet so that he clave it to the skull. He was so stunned that he fell to earth; and Aucassin put out his hand and took him prisoner, and led him off by the noseguard of his helmet, and delivered him to his father.

" Father," said Aucassin, " see here is your enemy who has made war on you so long and done you hurt so great. Twenty years has this war lasted, and never a man to put an end to it."

" Fair son," said his father, " well were it you should do deeds like this, and not gape at folly! "

"Father," said Aucassin, "read me no lectures, but keep me my covenant! "

" Bah! what covenant, fair son? "

" Alack, father, have you forgotten it? By the head of me, forget it who may, I do not mean to forget it. Rather have I laid it much to heart. Did you not make this covenant with me, that if I took arms and went out to the fighting, and if God brought me back safe and sound, you would let me see Nicolette my sweet friend for such time as I might speak two words to her or three, and once only kiss her? This covenant you made with me, and this covenant I will have you keep with me! "

" What, I? " said his father. " Ne'er help me Heaven if I keep this covenant with you! and were she here now I would burn her in a fire; and for yourself too you might fear the worst."

" Is this the whole conclusion?" said Aucassin.

" Aye," said his father, " so help me Heaven! "

"I' faith," said Aucassin, "then I am very sorry that a man of your age should be a liar. – Count of Valence, you are my prisoner."

" Sir, it is even so," said the Count.

" Give me your hand! " said Aucassin.

" Sir, right willingly."

He put his hand in his.

" This you pledge me," said Aucassin, " that never in all your days to be shall it be in your power to do shame to my father or to do hurt to him or his, and you not do it!
"

" Sir," said he, " for God's sake, mock me not, but set me a ransom! You can ask me nothing, gold or silver, war-horses or palfreys, sables or ermines, hounds or hawks, that I will not give you."

"How now?" said Aucassin. " Wot you not that you are my prisoner?"

" Aye, sir," said the Count Bulgarius.

" Ne'er help me Heaven," said Aucassin,"save you give me this pledge, if I send not your head a-flying! "

" I' God's name," said he, " I give you what pledge you please! "

He gave the pledge; and Aucassin set him on a horse, and himself mounted another, and conducted him till he was in safety.

Here they sing.

WhenCount Warren saw indeed
That he never will succeed
Aucassin his son to get
From bright-favoured Nicolette,
In a pris'n he had him set,
In a dungeon hid from day,
Builded all of marble grey.
Now when Aucassin came there
Sad he was – so was he ne'er.
Loud lamenting he fell on,
Thus as you shall hear anon.
" Flow'r o' the lily, Nicolette!
Bright-faced sweetheart, Nicolette!
Sweet as cluster of the vine,
Sweet as meed in maselyn.
This I saw some yesterday,
How a pilgrim on his way –
Limousin his land was – lay
Fevered on a bed within.
Grievous had his sickness been,
Great the fever he was in.
By his bedside Nicolette
Passing, lifted skirts and let –
'Neath the pretty ermine frock,
'Neath the snowy linen smock –
Just a dainty ankle show.
Lo, the sick was healed, and lo,
Found him whole as ne'er before.
From his bed he rose once more,
And to his own land did flit,
Safe and sound, whole ever whit.
Flow'r o' the lily, Nicolette!
Coming, going, ever pleasing,
In thy talk and in thy teasing,

In thy jest and in thy joying,
In thy kisses, in thy coying!
There is none could hate thee, dear!
Yet for thy sake am I here,
In this dungeon hid from day,
Where I cry Ah, well-a-way!
Now to die behoveth me,
Sweet friend, for thee! "

Here they speak and tell the story.

Aucassinwas put in prison, as you have listened and heard, and Nicolette was elsewhere in the chamber. 'Twas the summer time, the month of May, when the days are warm and long and bright, and the nights still and cloudless. Nicolette lay one night in her bed, and saw the moon shine bright through a window, and heard the nightingale sing in the garden; and she remembered Aucassin her friend, whom she loved so well. Then she fell a-thinking of Warren Count of Beaucaire, and how he hated her to death; and she thought within herself that she would abide there no longer; since if she were betrayed and Count Warren knew of her, he would put her to an evil death. She perceived that the old woman who was with her slept. And she arose and clad her in a goodly gown that she had of cloth-of-silk; and she took bedclothes and towels, and tied one to other and made a rope as long as she could, and made it fast to the window-shaft; and so got down into the garden. Then she took her dress in one hand before, and in the other behind, and girded herself, because of the dewshe saw heavy on the grass, and went her way down the garden. She had golden hair in little curls, and laughing blue eyes, and a face finely curved, and a proud shapely nose, and lips more red than cherry or rose in summertime, and small white teeth, and little breasts that swelled beneath her clothes like two nuts of a walnut- tree. And her waist was so fine that your two hands could have girdled her; and the daisy-flowers snapped by her toes, and lying on the arch of her foot, were fairly black beside her feet and ankles, so very white the girl was.

She came to the postern, and unfastened it, and went out through the streets of Beaucaire, keeping to the shadow, for the moon shone very bright; and she went on till she came to the tower where her friend was. The tower had cracks in it here and there, and she crouched against one of the piers, and wrapped herself in her mantle, and thrust her head into a chink in the tower, which was old and ancient, and heard Aucassin within weeping and making very great sorrow, and lamenting for his sweet friend whom he loved so much. And when she had listened enough to him she began to speak.

Here they sing.

Nicolettethe bright of face
Leaned her at the buttress-base,
Heard within her lover dear
Weeping and bewailing her;
Then she spake the thought in her:
" Aucassin, most gentle knight,
High-born lording, honoured wight,

What avails you to weep so?
What your wailing, what your woe?
I may ne'er your darling be,
For your father hateth me;
All your kin thereto agree.
For your sake I'll pass the sea,
Get me to some far countrie."
Tresses of her hair she clipped,
And within the tower slipped.
Aucassin, that lover true,
Took them and did honour due,
Fondly kissed them and caressed,
And bestowed them in his breast.
Then in tears anew he brake
For his love's sake.

Here they speak and tell the story.

WhenAucassin heard Nicolette say that she would depart into another country, he felt nothing but anger.

" Fair sweet friend," said he, " you shall not depart, for then would you have killed me. The first man that set eyes on you and could do so would straightway lay hands on you and take you to be his concubine. And once you had lived with any man but me, now dream not that I should wait to find a knife wherewith to strike me to the heart and kill me! Nay, verily, that were all too long to wait. Rather would I fling me just so far as I might see a bit of wall, or a grey stone; and against that would I dash my head so hard that my eyes should start out and all my brains be scattered. Yet even such a death would I die rather than know you had lived with any man but me."

" Ah! " said she, " I trow not that you love me so well as you say; but I love you better than you do me."

" Alack! " said Aucassin, "fair sweet friend! That were not possible that you should love meso well as I do you. Woman cannot love man so well as man loves woman. For a woman's love lies in her eye, in bud of bosom or tip of toe. But a man's love is within him, rooted in his heart, whence it cannot go forth."

While Aucassin and Nicolette were talking together, the town watch came down a street. They had their swords drawn under their cloaks, for Count Warren had given them command that if they could lay hands on her they should kill her. And the watchman on the tower saw them coming, and heard that they were talking of Nicolette and threatening to kill her.

" Great Heavens! " he said, " what pity it were should they slay so fair a maid! 'Twere a mighty good deed if I could tell her, in such wise that they perceived it not, and she could be ware of them. For if they slay her, then will Aucassin my young lord die; and that were great pity."

Here they sing.

Valiantwas the watch on wall,
Kindly, quick of wit withal.
He struck up a roundelay

Very seasonably gay.

" Maiden of the noble heart,
Winsome fair of form thou art;
Winsome is thy golden hair,
Blue thine eye and blithe thine air.
Well 1 see it by thy cheer,
Thou hast spoken with thy fere,
Who for thee lies dying here.
This I tell thee, thou give ear!
'Ware thee of the sudden foe!
Yonder seeking thee they go.
'Neath each cloak a sword I see;
Terribly they threaten thee.
Soon they'll do thee some misdeed
Save thou take heed! " 1

Here they speak and tell the story.

"! " said Nicolette; " now may thy father's soul and thy mother's be in blessed repose, for

The device of the warder is to give his warning in the guise of an*Aubade*as if he were merely singing for his own amusement. The*Aubade,*or Watch-song, was a favourite lyrical form in Southern France. Itthe grace and for the courtesy with which thou hast told me! Please God I will guard me well from them, and may God Himself be my guard! "

She wrapped her mantle about her in the shadow of the pier, till they had passed. Then she took leave of Aiicassin and went her way till she came to the castle wall. There was a breach in it which had been boarded up. On to this she climbed, and so got over between the wall and the ditch; and looking down she saw the ditch was very deep and the sides very sheer, and she was sore afraid.

"Ah, gracious Heaven!" she said; "if I let myself fall I shall break my neck; and if I abide here, I shall be taken to-morrow and burned in a fire. Nay, I had liefer die here than be made a show to-morrow for all the folk to stare at! "

She crossed herself, and let herself slip down into the ditch. And when she came to the bottom, her fair feet and her fair hands, untaught that ought could hurt them, were bruised and

was originally a dialogue between the lover, the lady, and the watchman who played sentinel, and warned them that the Dawn was coming.

torn, and the blood flowed in full a dozen places. Nevertheless she felt neither hurt nor pain for her great dread. And if she were troubled as to the getting in, she was far more troubled as to the getting out. But she bethought her that it was no good to linger there; and she found a sharpened stake which had been thrown by those within in the defence of the castle; and with this she made steps one above the other, and with much difficulty climbed up till she reached the top.

Now hard by was the forest, within two bowshots. It stretched full thirty leagues in length and in breadth, and had wild beasts in it and snaky things. She was afraid that if she went into it, these would kill her; and on the other hand she bethought her that if she were found there she would be taken back to the town to be burned.

Here they sing.

Nicolette, that bright-faced may,
Up the moat had won her way,
And to waymenting did fall,
And on Jesu's name 'gan call:
" Father, King of Majesty!
Now I wot not which way fly.
Should I to the greenwood hie,
There the wolves will me devour,
And the lions and wild boar,
Whereof yonder is great store.
Should I wait the daylight clear,
So that they should find me here,
Lighted will the fire bin
That my b'ody shall burn in.
But, O God of Majesty!
I had liefer yet fairly
That the wolves should me devour,
And the lions and wild boar,
Than into the city fare!
I'll not go there."

Here they speak and tell the story.

Nicolettemade great lamentation, as you have heard. She commended herself to God, and went on till she came into the forest. She durst not go deep into it, for the wild beasts and the snaky things; and she crept into a thick bush, and sleep fell on her. She slepttill the morrow at high Prime, when the herd- boys came out of the town, and drove their beasts between the wood and the river. They drew aside to a very beautiful spring which was at the edge of the forest, and spread out a cloak and put their bread on it. While they were eating, Nicolette awoke at the cry of the birds and of the herd-boys, and she sprang towards them.

" Fair children! " said she, " may the Lord help you! "

" May God bless you! " said the one who was more ready of speech than the others.

" Fair children," said she, " know you Aucassin, the son of the Count Warren of Beaucaire? "

" Yes, we know him well."

" So God help you, fair children," said she, " tell him that there is a beast in this forest, and that he come to hunt it. And if he can catch it he would not give one limb of it for a hundred marks of gold, no, not for five hundred, nor for any wealth."

And they gazed at her, and when they saw her so beautiful they were all amazed.

" What, I tell him? " said he who was more ready of speech than the others. " Sorrow behis whoever speak of it or whoever tell him! 'Tis fantasy that you say, since there is not so costly a beast in this forest, neither stag nor lion nor wild boar, one of whose limbs were worth more than two pence, or three at the most; and you speak of so great wealth! Foul sorrow be his who believe you, or whoever tell him! You are a fay, and we have no care for your company. So keep on your way!"

" Ah, fair children! " said she, " this will you do! The beast has such a medicine that Aucassin will be cured of his hurt. And I have here five sous in my purse; take them, so you tell him! Aye, and within three days must he hunt it, and, if in three days he find it not, never more will he be cured of his hurt! "

" I' faith! " said he, " the pence will we take; and if he come here we will tell him, but we will never go to seek him."

" I' God's name! " said she.

Then she took leave of the herdboys, and went her way.

Here they sing.

Nicolette, that bright-faced may,
From the herdboys went her way,
And her journeying addressed
Through the leafy thick forest,
Down a path of olden day,
Till she came to a highway,
Where do seven roads divide
Through the land to wander wide.
Then she fell bethinking her
She will try her true lover
If he love her as he sware.
Flow'rs o' the lily gathered she,
Branches of the jarris-tree,
And green leaves abundantly.
And she built a bower of green;
Daintier was there never seen.
By the truth of Heaven she sware,
That should Aucassin come there,
And a little rest not take
In the bower for her sweet sake,
Ne'er shall he her lover be,
Nor his love she!

Here they speak and tell the story.

Nicolettehad made the bower, as you have harkened and heard; very pretty she made it and very dainty, and all bedecked within and without with flowers and leaves. Then she laid her down near to the bower in a thick bush, to see what Aucassin would do.

And the cry and the noise went through all the land and through all the country that Nicolette was lost. There are some say that she is fled away; other some that the Count Warren has had her done to death. Rejoice who might, Aucassin was not well pleased. Count Warren his father bade take him out of prison; and summoned the knights of the land, and the damozels, and made a very rich feast, thinking to comfort Aucassin his son. But while the feasting was at its height, there was Aucassin leaned against a balcony, all sorrowful and all downcast. Make merry who might, Aucassin had no taste for it; since he saw nothing there of that he loved. A knight looked upon him, and came to him, and accosted him:

" Aucassin," said he, " of such sickness as yours, I too have been sick. I will give you good counsel, if you will trust me."

" Sir," said Aucassin, " gramercy! Good counsel should I hold dear."

" Mount on a horse," said he, " and go by yon forest side to divert you; there you will see the flowers and green things, and hear the birds sing. Peradventure you shall hear a word for which you shall be the better."

" Sir," said Aucassin, "gramercy! So will I do."

He stole from the hall, and descended the stairs, and came to the stable where his horse was. He bade saddle and bridle him; and setting foot in stirrup, he mounted and rode forth out of the castle, and went on till he came to the forest. He rode till he reached the spring, and came upon the herdboys at the point of None. They had spread a cloak on the grass, and were eating their bread and making very great merriment.

Here they sing.

Camethe herds from every part in;
There was Esme, there was Martin;
There was Fruelin and Johnny;
Aubrey boon, and Robin bonny.
Then to speech did one address him:
" Mates, young Aucassin, God bless him!
'Struth, it is a fine young fellow!
And the girl with hair so yellow,
With the body slim and slender,
Eyes so blue and bloom so tender!
She that gave us such a penny
As shall buy us sweetmeats many,
Hunting-knife and sheath of leather,
Flute and fife to play together,
Scrannel pipe and cudgel beechen.
I pray God leech him! "

This piece of verse is remarkable for the evident intention of playfulness in it. All the lines end in a diminutive termination, and all the proper names also; Esmeret, Martinet, Fruelin, Johanet, Aubriet, Aucassinet. It seemed impossible to preserve this playfulness in any direct way, without sacrifice of literal rendering and without changing the proper names. I have tried to give a little of it by the use of dissyllabic rhymes.

Here they speak and tell the story.

WhenAucassin heard the shepherd boys, he minded him of Nicolette his most sweet friend whom he loved so well; and he bethought him that she had been there. And he pricked his horse with the spurs, and came to the shepherd boys.

" Fair children, may God help you! "

" May God bless you! " said he who was more ready of speech than the others.

" Fair children," said he, " say again the song that you were saying just now! "

" We will not say it," said he who was more ready of speech than the others. "
Sorrow be his who sings it for you, fair sir! "

Fair children," said Aucassin, " do you not know me?"

" Aye, we know well that you are Aucassin, our young lord; but we are not your
men, but the Count's."

" Fair children, you will do so, I pray you! "

" Hear, by gog's heart! " said he. " And why should I sing for you, an it suit me
not? When there is no man in this land so rich,

saving Count Warren's self, who finding my oxen or my cows or my sheep in his
pastures or in his crops, would dare to chase them from it, for fear of having his eyes
put out. And why should I sing for you, an it suit me not?"

" So God help you, fair children, you will do so! And take ten sous which 1 have
here in a purse! "

" Sir, the pence will we take, but I will not sing to you, for I have sworn it. But I
will tell it to you, if you will."

" F God's name! " said Aucassin; " I had liefer telling than nothing."

" Sir, we were here just now, between Prime and Tierce, and were eating our bread
at this spring, even as we are doing now. And a maiden came here, the most beautiful
thing in the world, so that we deemed it was a f<iy, and all the wood lightened with
her. And she gave us of what was hers, so that we covenanted with her, if you came
here, we would tell you that you are to go a-hunting in this forest. There is a beast
there which, could you catch it, you would not give one of its limbs for five hundred
marks of silver, nor for any wealth. For the beast has such a medicine that if you
can catch ityou will be cured of your hurt. Aye, and within three days must you have
caught it, and if you have not caught it, never more will you see it. Now hunt it an
you will, or an you will leave it; for I have well acquitted myself towards her."

" Fair children," said Aucassin, " enough have you said; and God grant me to find
it! "

Here they sing.
Aucassinhas word for word
Of his lithe-limbed lady heard;
Deep they pierced him to the quick;
From the herds he parted quick,
Struck into the greenwood thick.
Quickly stepped his gallant steed,
Bore him fairly off full speed.
Then he spake, three words he said:
" Nicolette, O lithe-limbed maid!
For your sake I thrid the glade!
Stag nor boar I now pursue,
But the sleuth I track for you!
Your bright eyes and body lithe,
Your sweet words and laughter blithe,
Wounded have my heart to death.
So God, the strong Father will,

I shall look upon you still,
Sister, sweet friend! "
Here they speak and tell the story.

Aucassinwent through the forest this way and that way, and his good steed carried him a great pace. Think not that the briars and thorns spared him! Not a whit! Nay they tore his clothes so, that 'twere hard work to have patched them together again; and the blood flowed from his arms and his sides and his legs in forty places or thirty; so that one could have followed the boy by the trace of the blood that fell upon the grass. But he thought so much on Nicolctte, his sweet friend, that he felt neither hurt nor pain. All day long he rode through the forest, but so it was that he never heard news of her. And, when he saw that evening drew on, he began to weep because he found her not.

He was riding down an old grassy road, when he looked before him in the way and saw a boy, and I will tell you what he was like. He was tall of stature and wonderful to see, so ugly and hideous. He had a monstrous shock-head black as coal, and there was more than a full palm- breadth between his two eyes; and he had great cheeks, and an immense flat nose, with great wide nostrils, and thick lips redder than a roast, and great ugly yellow teeth. He was shod in leggings and shoes of ox-hide, laced with bast to above the knee; and was wrapped in a cloak which seemed inside out either way on, and was leaning on a great club. Aucassin sprang to meet him, and was terrified at the nearer sight of him.

" Fair brother, may God help you! "

" May God bless you! " said he.

" So God help you, what do you there?"

" What matters it to you? " said he.

"Nothing "; said Aucassin; " Task not for any ill reason."

" But wherefore are you weeping," said he, " and making such sorrow? I' faith, were 1 as rich a man as you are, all the world would not make me weep! "

" Bah! Do you know me? " said Aucassin.

" Aye. I know well that you are Aucassin the son of the Count; and if you tell me wherefore you are weeping I will tell you what I am doing here."

" Certes," " said Aucassin, " I will tell you right willingly. I came this morning to hunt in this forest; and I had a white greyhound, the fairest in the world, and I have lost it; 'tis for this I am weeping."

" Hear him! " said he, " by the blessed heart! and you wept for a stinking dog! Sorrow be his who ever again hold you in account! Why there is no man in this land so rich, of whom if your father asked ten, or fifteen, or twenty, he would not give them only too willingly, and be only too glad. Nay, 'tis I should weep and make sorrow."

" And wherefore you, brother? "

" Sir, I will tell you. I was hireling to a rich farmer, and drove his plough – four oxen there were. Three days since a great misfortune befell me. I lost the best of my oxen, Roget, the best of my team; and I have been in search of it ever since. I have neither eaten nor drunk these three days past; and I dare not go into the town, as they would put me in prison, since I have not wherewith to pay for it. Worldly goods have I none worth ought but what you see on the body of me. I have a mother, poorwoman, who had nothing worth ought save one poor mattress, and this they have dragged from under her back, so that she lies on the bare straw; and for her I am troubled a deal more than for myself. For wealth comes and goes; if I have lost now I shall gain another time, and I shall pay for my ox when I can; nor will I ever weep for an ox. And you wept for a dog of the dunghill! Sorrow be his wlio ever again hold you in account! "

" Certes, you are of good comfort, fair brother! Bless you for it! And what was thine ox worth? "

" Sir, it is twenty sous they ask me for it; I cannot abate a single farthing."

" Here," said Aucassin, " take these twenty which I have in my purse, and pay for thine ox!"

"Sir," said he, "Gramercy! And may God grant you to find that which you seek!"

He took leave of him; and Aucassin rode on. The night was fine and still; and he went on till he came to the place where the seven roads divide, and there before him he saw the bower which Nicolette had made, bedecked within and without and over and in front with flowers, andso pretty that prettier could not be. When Aucassin perceived it, he drew rein all in a moment; and the light of the moon smote within it.

" Ah, Heaven! " said Aucassin, " here has Nicolette been, my sweet friend; and this did she make with her beautiful hands! For the sweetness of her, and for her love, I will now alight here, and rest me there this night through."

He put his foot out of the stirrup to alight. His horse was big and high; and he was thinking so much on Nicolette, his most sweet friend, that he fell on a stone so hard that his shoulder flew out of place. He felt that he was badly hurt; but he bestirred him the best he could, and tied his horse up with his other hand to a thorn; and he turned over on his side, so that he got into the bower on his back. And he looked through a chink in the bower, and saw the stars in the sky; and he saw one there brighter than the rest, and he began to say:

Here they sing.

"Littlestar, I see thee there,
That the moon draws close to her!
Nicolette is with thee there,
My love of the golden hair.
God, I trow, wants her in Heaven
To become the lamp of even.
Whatsoe'er the fall might be,
Would I were aloft with thee!
Straitly I would kiss thee there.
Though a monarch's son I were,
Yet would you befit me fair,
Sister, sweet friend! "

Here they speak and tell the story.

WhenNicolette heard Aucassin she came to him, for she was not far off. She came into

Three lines are torn away in the original MS.

the bower, and threw her arms round his neck, and kissed and caressed him.

" Fair sweet friend, well be you met! "

" And you, fair sweet friend, be you the well met! "

They kissed and caressed each other, and their joy was beautiful.

" Ah, sweet friend! " said Aucassin, " I was but now sore hurt in my shoulder; and now I feel neither hurt nor pain since I have you! "

She felt about, and found that he had his shoulder out of place. She plied it so with her white hands, and achieved (as God willed, who loveth lovers) that it came again into place. And then she took flowers and fresh grass and green leaves, and bound them on with the lappet of her smock, and he was quite healed.

" Aucassin," said she, "fair sweet friend, take counsel what you will do! If your father makes them search this forest to-morrow, and they find me – whatever may become of you, they will kill me! "

" Cert$s, fair sweet friend, I should be much grieved at that! But, an I be able, they shall never have hold of you! " He mounted on his horse, and took his love in front of him, kissing and caressing her; and they set out into the open fields.

Here they sing.

Aucassin, the boon, the blond,
High-born youth and lover fond,
Rode from out the deep forest;
In his arms his love he pressed,
'Fore him on the saddle-bow;
Kisses her on eyes and brow,
On her mouth and on her chin.
Then to him did she begin:
" Aucassin, fair lover sweet,
To what land are we to fleet? "
" Sweet my sweetheart, what know I?
Nought to me 'tis where we fly,
In greenwood or utter way,
So I am with you alway! "
So they pass by dale and down,
By the burgh and l>y the town,
At daybreak the sea did reach,
And alighted on the beach
'Longside the strand.

Here they speak and tell the story.

Aucassinhad alighted, he and his love together, as you have harkened and heard. He held his horse by the bridle and his love by the hand, and they began to go along the shore; and they went on till Aucassin descried some merchants who were in a ship sailing near the shore. He beckoned to them and they came to him; and he dealt with them so that they took him into their ship. And when they were on the high sea a storm arose, great and wonderful, which carried them from land to land, till they arrived at a foreign land, and entered the port of the castle of Torelore. Then they asked what land it was; and they told them that it was the land of the king of Torelore. Then he asked, Who was he, and was there war? And they told him:

"Yes, great war."

He took leave of the merchants, and theycommended him to God. He mounted his horse, with his sword girt, and his love before him, and went on till he came to the castle. He asked where the king was, and they told him that he lay in child-bed.

" And where then is his wife? "

And they told him that she was with the army, and had taken thither all the folk of the land. And when Aucassin heard it, he thought it a very strange thing; and he came to the palace, and alighted, he and his love together. And she held his horse, and he went up to the palace, with his sword girt; and went on till he came to the room where the king lay a-bed.

Here they sing.

Aucassinthe room ent'red,
He the courteous, the high-bred,
And went straight up to the bed,
On the which the king was laid.
Right in front of him he stayed,
And so spake, hear what he said:
" Go to, fool! What dost thou there?"
Quoth the king: " A son I bear.
Soon as is my month fulfilled,
And I am quite whole and healed,
Then shall I the mass go hear,
As my ancestor did ere,
And my great war to maintain
'Gainst mine enemies again.
I will not leave it! "

Here they speak and tell the story.

WhenAucassin heard the king speak thus, he took all the clothes which were on him, and flung them down the room. He saw behind him a stick. He took it, and turned and struck him, and beat him so that he was like to have killed him.

The custom of a husband taking to his bed when his wife has borne a child is a curious superstition well-known to ethnologists and folk-lore students. The convenient name of*Couvade,*though originally applied to this custom by a mistake, has now become recognised, and it seems best to retain it.

"Ah, fair sir!" said the king, "what is it you ask of me? Have you your wits distraught, you who beat me in my own house? "

" By the heart of God," said Aucassin, " you whoreson knave, I will kill you unless you give me your word that never more shall any man in your land lie in child-bed! "

He gave him his word; and when he had given it,

" Sir," said Aucassin, " now take me where your wife is with the army! "

" Sir, right willingly! " said the king.

He mounted a horse, and Aucassin mounted his; and Nicolette remained in the queen's chambers. And the king and Aucassin rode till they came where the queen was; and they found it a battle of crab-apples roasted, and eggs, and fresh cheeses. And Aucassin began to gaze at them, and he wondered very hard.

Here they sing.

Aucassinhas stayed him so,
Elbow-propped on saddle-bow,
And began a-gazing at
This tremendous pitched combat.
They had brought with them thereto
Store of cheeses enow new,
Wild crab-apples roasted through,
And of great field-mushrooms too.
He who best disturbs the fords
Is proclaimed the chief of lords.
Aucassin, the gallant knight,
'Gan a-gazing at the sight,
And fell a-laughing.

Here they speak and tell the story.

WhenAucassin saw this strange thing, he came to the king and accosted him:

" Sir," said Aucassin, " are these your enemies?"

" Yes, sir," said the king.

"And would you that I should avenge you of them? "

"Yes," said he, "willingly."

And Aucassin put his hand to his sword, and dashed in among them, and began tostrike to right and to left, and killed many of them. And when the king saw that he was killing them he took him by the bridle, and said,

" Ah, fair sir! Do not kill them so! "

" How? " said Aucassin. " Do you not wish that I should avenge you?"

" Sir," said the king, " you have done it overmuch. It is not our custom to kill one another."

The other side turned to flight; and the king and Aucassin returned to the Castle of Torelore. And the people of the country bade the king drive Aucassin out of his land, and keep Nicolette for his son, since she seemed in sooth a lady of high degree. And when Nicolette heard it she was not well-pleased; and she began to ay,

Here they sing.

"Kingof Torelore! " she said,
Nicolette the lovely maid,
" Fool I seem in your folk's sight!
When my sweet friend clips me tight,
Smooth and soft for his delight,
Then am I at such a school,
Ball nor dance nor gay carole,
Harp nor viol nor cithole,
Nor the pleasures of*nimpo/e,*
Were ought beside it! "

Here they speak and tell the story.

Aucassinwas at the Castle of Torelore, and Nicolette his love, in great content and in great delight, for he had with him Nicolette, his sweet friend whom he loved so well. While he was in such content and in such delight, a fleet of Saracens came by sea and attacked the castle and took it by storm. They took the stuff, and led away men-captives and women-captives. They took Nicolette and Aucassin, and bound Aucassin hand and foot and threw him into one

It is unknown what the game of *NimpoleNypMcte* was. But elsewhere it is coupled with games played on a board, *jeux de tablet*, as if of the same nature as draughts or chess.

ship, and Nicolette into another. And there arose a storm at sea which parted them. The ship in which Aucassin was went drifting over the sea till it arrived at the Castle of Beaucaire. And when the people of the country ran to the wrecking of it, they found Aucassin, and recognised him. When the men of Beaucaire saw their young lord, they made great joy of him; for Aucassin had stayed at the Castle of Torelore full three years, and his father and mother were dead. They brought him to the Castle of Beaucaire, and all became his liegemen. And he held his land in peace.

Here they sing.
Aucassin did thus repair
To his city of Beaucaire;
All the kingdom and countrie
Held in great tranquillity.
Swore he by God's majesty,
Sorer far is his regret
For bright-favoured Nicolette
Than his kinsfolk every one,
Though they all were dead and gone.
" Sweet my sweetheart, bright of cheer,
You to seek I know not where!
Never God made that countrie,
Overland or oversea,
If I thought to light on thee,
I'd not fly thither! "
Here they speak and tell the story,
Now we will leave Aucassin, and tell of Nico- lette. The ship in which Nicolette was, was the king of Carthage's, and he was her father, and she had twelve brothers, all princes or kings. When they saw Nicolette so beautiful, they did her very great honour, and made rejoicing over her; and much they questioned of her who she was; for in sooth she seemed a very noble lady and of high degree. But she could not tell them who she was; for he had been carried captive as a little child.

They sailed till they came beneath the city of Carthage. And when Nicolette saw the walls of the castle, and the country, she recognised that it was there she had been brought up and carried captive as a little child; yet she was not such a little child but that she knew well that she had been daughter to the king of Carthage, and that she had been brought up in the city.

Here they ting.
Nicolette, the wise, the brave,
Won to land from off the wave;
Sees the wharves, the city walls,

And the palaces and halls;
Then she cries, " Ah! woe is me!
Ah, woe worth my high degree!
King's daughter of Carthagen,
To the Amiral akin!
Here me holds a salvage horde!
Aucassin, my gentle lord,
Wise and worshipful and free,
Your sweet love constrained! me,
Calleth me and troubleth me!
Grant me God the Heavenly
Yet to hold you in embrace,
And that you should kiss my face
And my mouth and all my cheer,
My liege lord dear! "
Here they speak and tell the story.

Whenthe king of Carthage heard Nicolette speak thus, he threw his arms round her neck.

"Fair sweet friend," said he, "tell me who you are! Be not afraid of me! "

" Sir," said she, " I am daughter to the king of Carthage, and was carried captive as a little child, full fifteen years ago."

When they heard her speak thus, they knew well that she said truly; and they made very great rejoicing over her, and brought her to the palace with great honour, as a king's daughter. A lord they wished to give her, a king of Paynim; but she had no care to wed. And when she had been there full three days or four, she considered with herself by what device she might go to seek Aucassin. She procured a viol and learned to play on it; till one day thqjr wished to marry her to a king, a rich Paynim. Then she stole away in the night, and came to the seaport, and harboured her at the house of a poor woman on the seashore.

And she took a herb, and smeared her head and face with it, so that she was all black and stained. And she got a coat made, and cloak and shirt and breeches, and attired herself in minstrel guise; and she took her viol, and went to a mariner, and so dealt with him that he took her in his ship. They set their sail, and sailed over the high sea till they arrived at the land of Provence. And Nicolette went forth, and took her viol, and went playing through the country, till she came to the Castle of Beaucaire, where Aucassin*Here they sing.*

Beaucaire beneath the tower
Aucassin was one fair hour.
Here he sat him on a stair;
Round him his proud barons were;
Saw the flower and green herb spring,
Heard the song-bird sweetly sing;
Of his love he thought anew,
Nicolette the maiden true,
Whom he loved so long a day;

Then to tears and sighs gave way.
Look you, Nicolette below
Draws her viol, draws her bow;
Now she speaks, her tale tells so:
" List to me, proud lords arow,
Those aloft and those alow!
Would it please you hear a word
Of Aucassin, a proud lord,
And of Nicolette the bold?
Long their love did last and hold
Till he sought her in the wold.
Then, from Torelore's stronghold,
They were haled by heathen horde.
Of Aucassin we've no word.
Nicolette the maiden bold
Is at Carthage the stronghold,
Whom her father dear doth hold
Who of yonder land is lord.
Husband they would her award,
Felon king of heathenesse.
Nicolette cares not for this,
For she loves a lording lad,
Aucassin to name he had.
By God and His name she vows
Never lord will she espouse,
If she have not her true love
She's so fain of."

Here they speak and tell the story.

WhenAucassin heard Nicolette speak thus, he was very glad, and he took her on one side, and asked her,

" Fair sweet comrade," said Aucassin, " know you ought of this Nicolette, of whom you have sung?"

" Sir, yes! I know of her as the noblest creature and the gentlest and wisest that ever was born. And she is daughter to the kingof Carthage, who took her when Aucassin was taken, and carried her to the city of Carthage, when he knew surely that she was his daughter, and made very great rejoicing over her. And every day they wish to give her for lord one of the highest kings in all Spain. But she would rather let herself be hanged or drowned than she would take any of them, were he ever so rich."

" Ah, fair sweet comrade," said the Count Aucassin, " if you would go back to that land, and would tell her to come and speak to me, 1 would give you of my wealth as much as you should dare ask or take. Know, moreover, that for the love of her I will take no wife, were she of ever so high degree, but I wait for her; nor will I ever have any wife save her. And had I known where to find her I should not now have to seek her."

" Sir," said she, " if you would do this, I would go to seek her, for your sake, and for hers, whom I love much."

He sware to her; and then he bade give her twenty pounds. And as she took leave of him, he fell weeping for the sweetness of Nicolette. And when she saw him weeping,

" Sir," said she, " be not afraid! Sincewithin a little while I will bring her to you in this town, so that you shall see her."

And when Aucassin heard it he was very glad. And she took leave of him, and went into the town to the house of the Viscountess; for the Viscount her godfather was dead. She harboured her there; and spoke with her till she confessed her affair to her, and the Viscountess recognised her, and knew surely that it wa Nicolette, and that she had brought her up. And she made her be washed and bathed, and sojourn there a full eight days. And she took a plant which was called Celandine and anointed herself with it, and she was as beautiful as she had ever been at any time. And she clad herself in rich silk stuffs, of which the lady had good store, and she sat her down in the room on a quilted coverlet of cloth-of-silk, and called the lady, and told her to go for Aucassin her friend. And she did so. And when she came to the palace she found Aucassin weeping and lamenting for Nicolette his love, because she tarried so long. And the lady accosted him and said:

" Aucassin, now make no more lament, but come away with me, and I will show you the thing in the world you love best, for it isNicolette, your sweet friend, who from far lands is come to seek you." And Aucassin was glad.

Hire they sing.

Now when Aucassin did hear
Of his bright-of-favour fere,
That she had arrived the shore,
Glad was he, he ne'er was more.
With the dame he went his way,
Till the house made stop nor stay.
To the chamber went they in
Where sat Nicolette within.
When she saw her lover there,
Glad she was, so was she ne'er.
Towards him to her feet leapt she.
Aucassin, when he did see,
Both his arms to her he holds,
Gently to his bosom folds,
Kisses her on eyes and face.
So they left him the night's space,
Till the morrow's morning-tide
Aucassin took her to bride,

Made her Lady of Beaucaire. Many days they then did fare, And their pleasure did enjoy. Now has Aucassin his joy, Nicolette too the same way. Here endeth our song-and-say; I know no further.

PRINTED BY
TURNBULL AND SPEARS, EDINBURGH THE NEOLITHIC PERIOD TO

THE DEATH OF CLEOPATRA
VII.(b. c.
WallisBudge, M. A., Litt. D., D. Litt., Keeper of the Egyptian and Assyrian
antiquities in the British Museum.

volt, profusely illustrated. Price per volume,

The only complete History of Ancient Egypt in the English language embodying
the results of all the latest researches.

"The best history of Ancient Egypt that has so far appeared in English. From first
to last the history has the living reality of a work written at first hand by; i scholar who
spends his life face to face with the monuments of the people whose development and
decay he traces in minute and authentic detail." – *Spectator.*

"A carefully studied and lavishly illustrated account, without technical harshness,
of what is known to learning concerning the history of the land of the Pharaohs before
the Christian era." – *Scotsman.*

"The publication of this work, certainly the most complete and exhaustive English
history of the Egyptian kingdom from the earliest times which we possess, may be
said without undue eulogy to mark an epoch in Egyptological studies in this country."
– *Glasgow Herald.*

"The work, while thoroughly scholarly in its narrative, has an easy, pleasant style,
which will recommend it to those who are not specialists, and all classes will be
grateful to the author for the voluminous index, map, and illustrations." – *Standard.*

KEGANPAUL, TRENCH, TRUBNKR&CO., Ltd.

4

SECTION 4

OF TO-DAY

An attempt at a critical estimate with biblio-

f rapines of the books illustrated by the chief artists, y R. E. D. Sketchley, with an introduction on old and new book illustrations byAlfredPollard.

The bibliographies have, whenever possible, been submitted to the artists themselves, so that they should form a trustworthy guide to collectors of modern illustrated books.

The introduction, which is itself illustrated with reproductions from various fifteenth century books, endeavours to show some of the points iu which lessons may still be learnt from the work of the old illustrators.

*Fcaf.*40, IOS. 6d.

Also a limited edition printed on Japanese Vellum. Particulars on application.

SHAKSPERE'S SONNETS AND POEMS

Edition de luxe. With an Introduction by ProfessorDowden. Printed on Arnold & Foster's handmade paper by Messrs T. & A. Constable, Edinburgh. Ornamental initials and tail-pieces specially designed by W. B. Macdougall. Printed in red and black in special antique faced type. Handsomely bound in vellum. Limited to 400 numbered copies for England.

*Narro'w demy*8-yj.*Puklithcd at*155.

There is also an edition limited to 30 copies for England printed on the finest Japanese vellum.

KEGANPAUL, TRENCH, TRUBNER&CO., Ltd.